The pivot is the human scale: the sleeping man at the picnic, captured in a view 1 meter square from 1 meter away. Our point of view is always perpendicular to this man. Therefore, every image on every page, out to the outermost power, is centered on the nucleus of an atom in the hand of the sleeping man. Following that path, this flipbook offers a journey of 38 powers of ten. It takes 2 pages per power. That means that starting at the front (big going towards small), every 2 pages you see a view ten times smaller than the view 2 pages earlier. Or if you are starting at the back (small going towards big), every two pages you see a view ten times larger than the view 2 pages earlier. Since every image is centered on the same ████ █████ given page is a detail from the center █████████████████████ ext lower page nested within it. [The i██████████████████████████ from a point approximately half way ████

Starting at th████████████████████████ time leaping 10 times further, we wou████████████████████ illion light years out, roughly 3 orders ███ D1198836 ████████ rvable universe. And, by diving in 15 p█████████████████████ utting our field of view down to a tenth █████████████████████ ive at 10^{-15} meters, the scale of a proton, or about 3 orders of magnitude from the scale of a quark. As you can confirm by counting the powers for yourself, if that tiny proton were one unit, then the biggest square (ten million light years) would be 10^{+38}, or 100,000,000,000,000,000,000,000,000,000,000,000,000 of those units.

The images in this flipbook come from the film <u>Powers of Ten</u> by Charles and Ray Eames, the husband and wife team ranked among the most important designers of the 20th Century. Best known for their furniture, they also made landmark contributions to architecture, graphics, and communications. One of their more than 100 short films, <u>Powers of Ten</u> expresses a key part of their design approach: the value of looking at things from the next largest frame of reference, and the next smallest. • <u>Powers of Ten</u> is also available on video, as an informative book, and, most recently, as a CD-ROM of 6 parallel adventures in scale. Contact the Eames Office for more information.

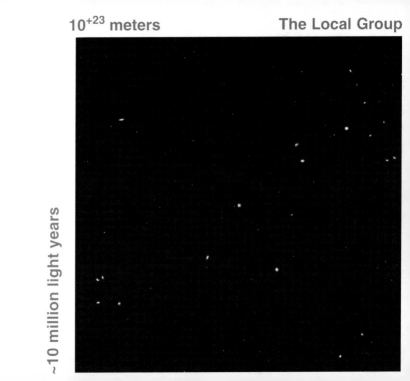

10^{+23} meters

The Local Group

~10 million light years

~1 million light years

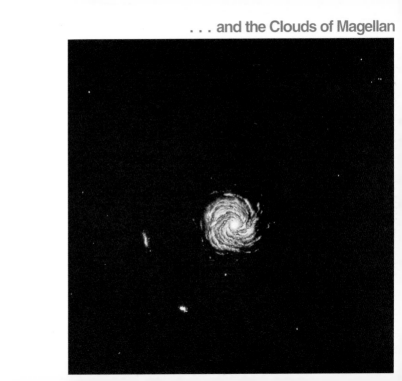

10^{+21} meters   The Milky Way

~100,000 light years

10^{+20} meters Clouds of stars and glowing gas . . .

~10,000 light years

~1,000 light years

10^{+18} meters   **That red star is Arcturus**

~100 light years

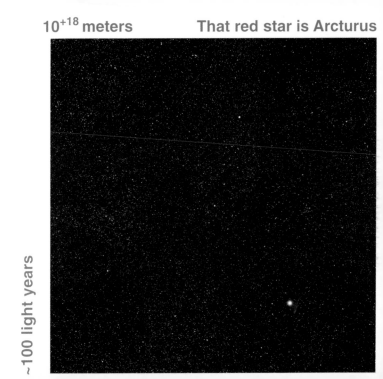

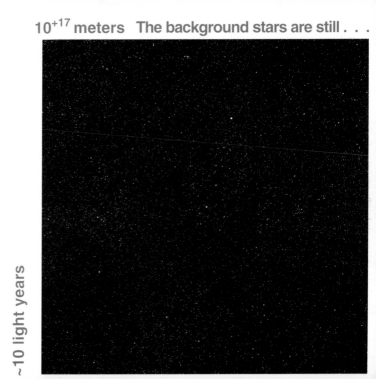

~10 light years

10^{+16} meters   . . . unchanged for several powers;

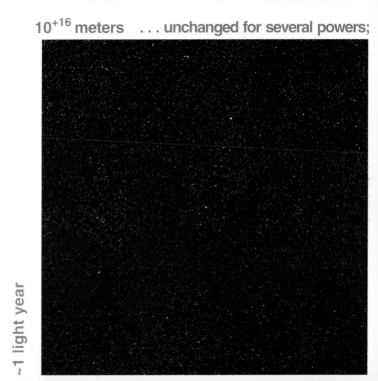

~1 light year

the dot in the center . . .

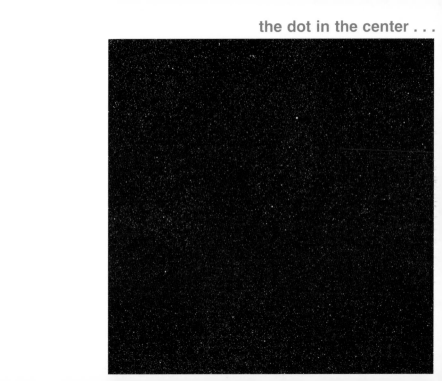

10⁺¹⁵ meters . . . is the distant Sun.

1 trillion kilometers

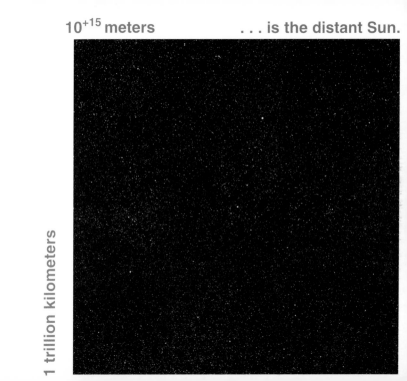

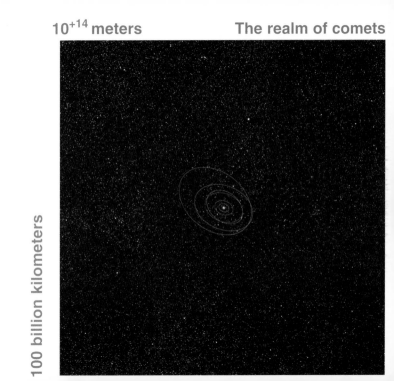

10^{+14} meters

The realm of comets

100 billion kilometers

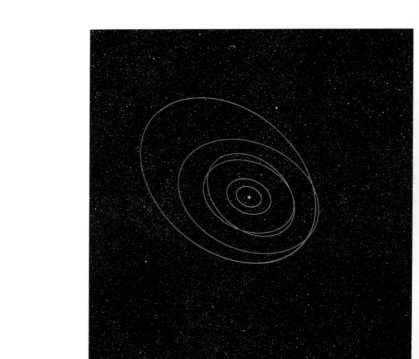

10^{+13} meters   Orbits of Pluto, Neptune, . . .

10 billion kilometers

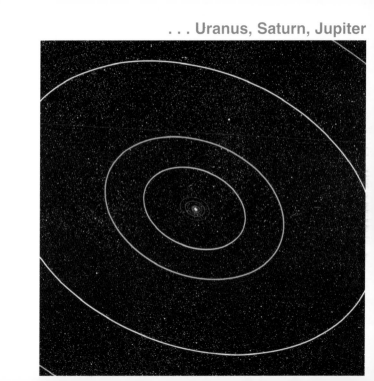

1 billion kilometers

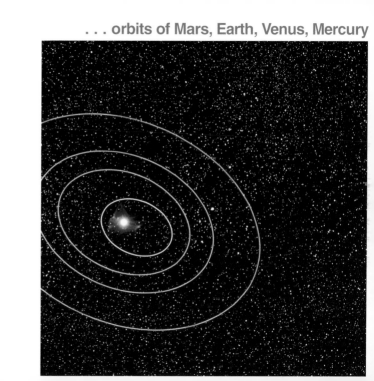

100 million kilometers

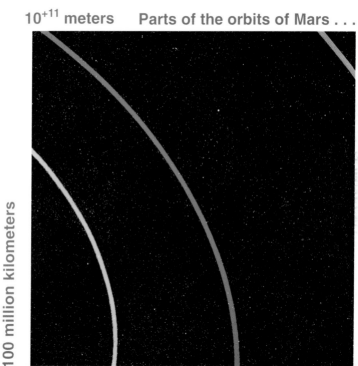

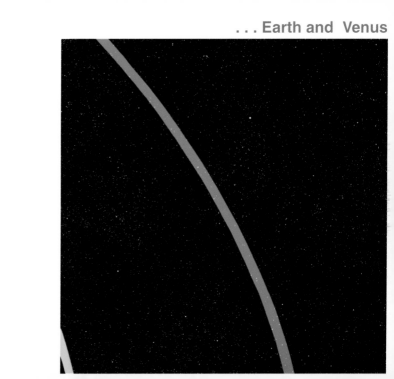

10^{+10} meters A portion of the Earth's path . . .

10 million kilometers

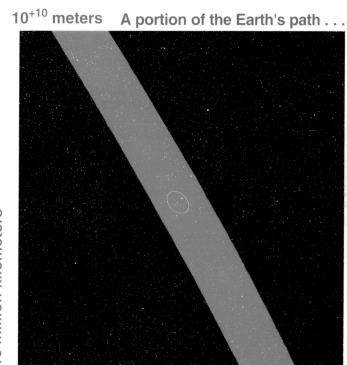

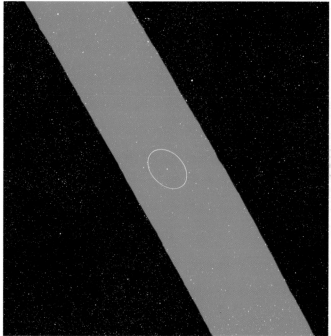

10⁺⁹ meters **The orbit of the Moon . . .**

1 million kilometers

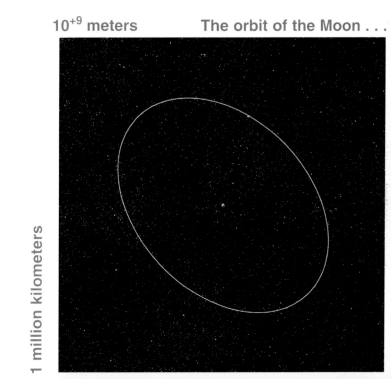

10^{+8} meters   The Earth against background stars

100,000 kilometers

10⁺⁷ meters — The Earth

10,000 kilometers

10^{+6} meters   Lake Michigan is fully visible

1,000 kilometers

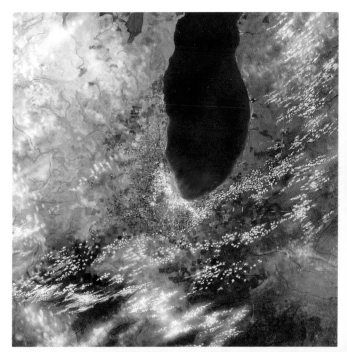

10⁺⁵ meters   The greater Chicago area

100 kilometers

10⁺⁴ meters   Chicago by the lake shore

10 kilometers

Soldier Field and . . .

1 kilometer

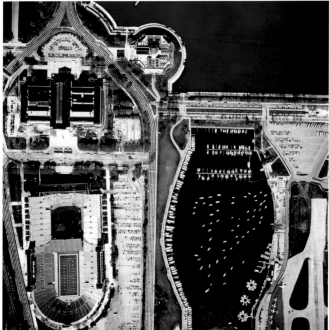

10^{+2} meters   Lake Shore Drive and the Marina

100 meters

10+1 meters

The picnic on the
lake front in Chicago

10 meters

1 meter

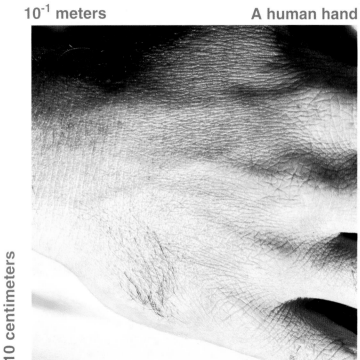

10⁻¹ meters

A human hand

10 centimeters

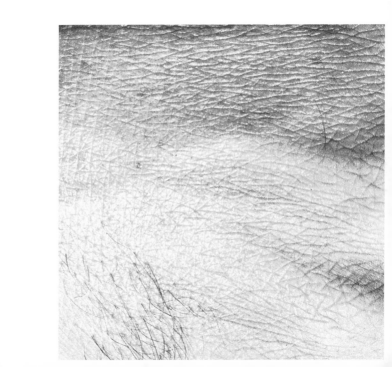

1 centimeter

1 millimeter

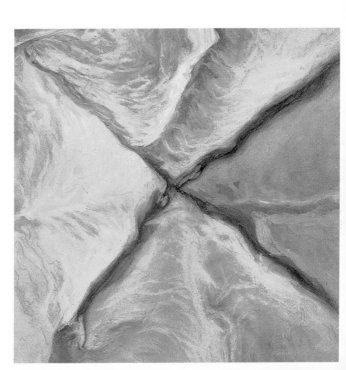

10^{-4} meters

The dermis

100 microns

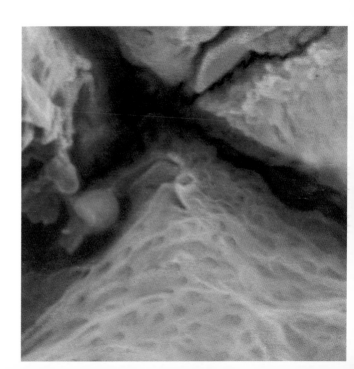

10^{-5} meters   A ruffly lymphocyte in a capillary . . .

Explaining the Transition: the ruffly lymphocyte seen at 10^{-5} is located in a capillary just beneath the surface of the hand.

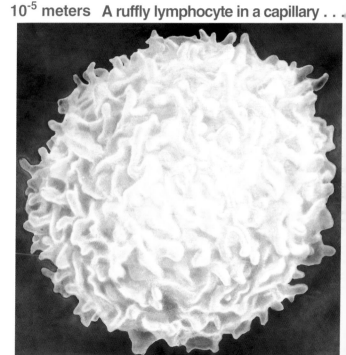

10 microns

. . . under the surface of the hand

10^{-6} meters   The wall of that cell's nucleus

Explaining the Transition: the dark surface seen at 10^{-6} is not a detail of the surface of the ruffly lymphocyte, but rather a detail of the nucleus of that cell.

1 micron

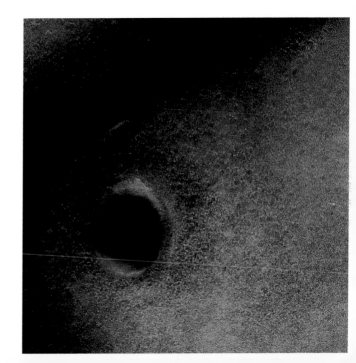

10⁻⁷ meters — DNA

1,000 angstroms (100 nanometers)

Explaining the Transition: the DNA you see at 10⁻⁷ is contained within the nucleus whose surface you see at the next larger image.

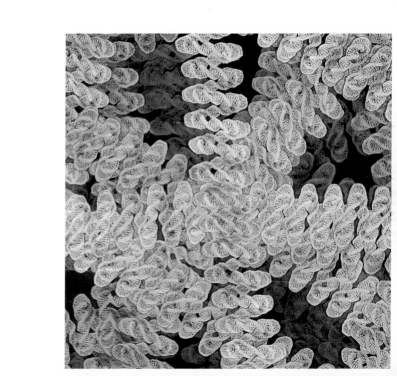

10⁻⁸ meters — DNA

100 angstroms (10 nanometers)

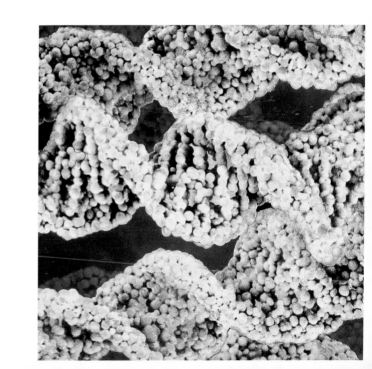

10⁻⁹ meters

Building blocks of DNA . . .

10 angstroms (1 nanometer)

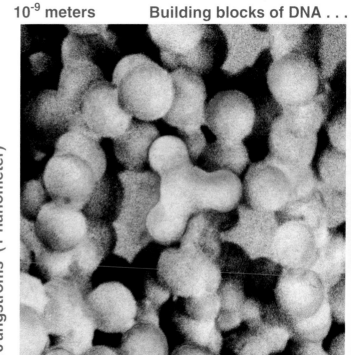

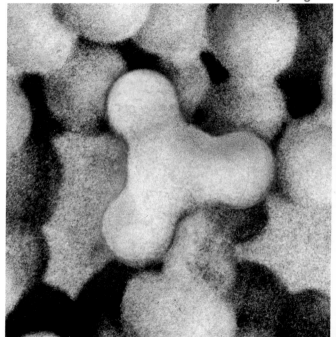

A carbon atom in the center, bonded to 3 hydrogens

10⁻¹⁰ meters   Outer electron shell of carbon atom

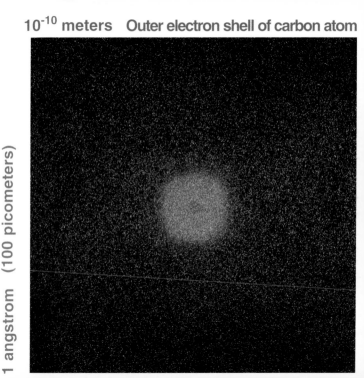

Explaining the Transition: the dots you see at 10⁻¹⁰ are a symbolic representation of the electron shell of one carbon atom.

1 angstrom   (100 picometers)

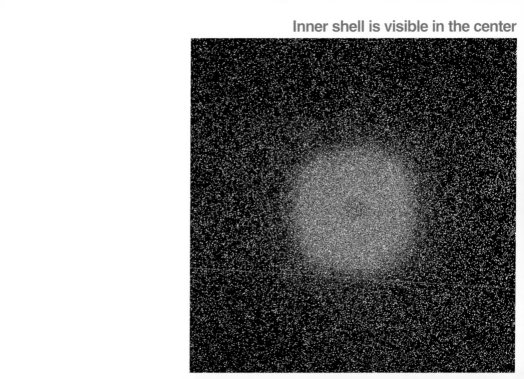

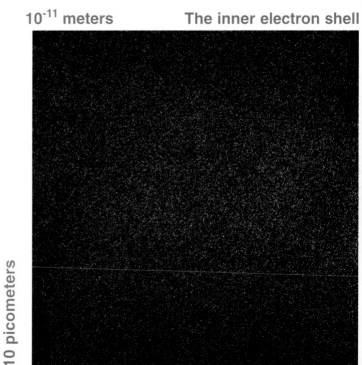

10⁻¹¹ meters The inner electron shell

10 picometers

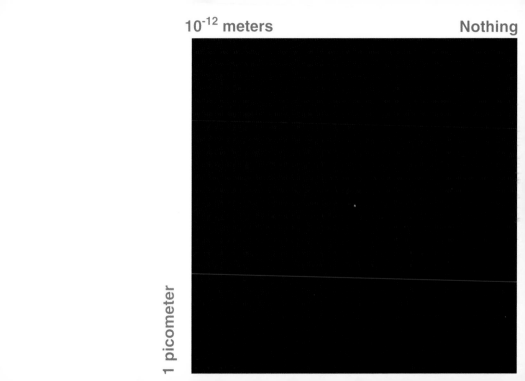

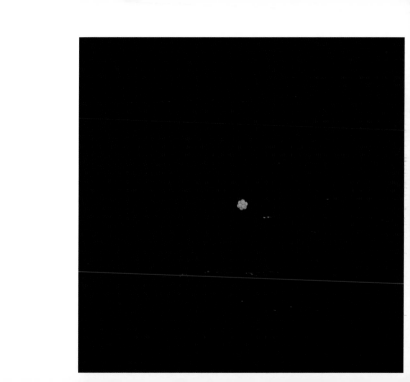

10^{-13} meters   Carbon nucleus in the distance

100 fermis

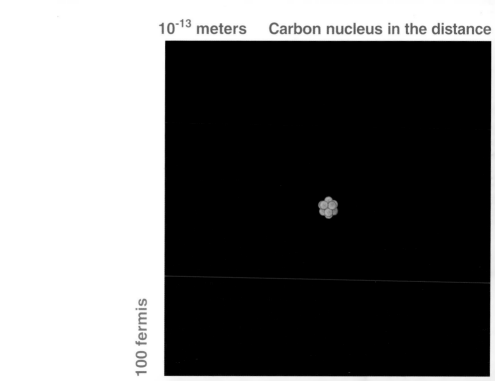

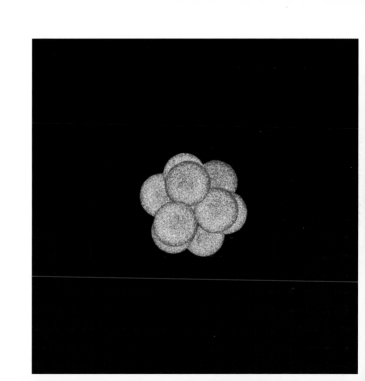

10⁻¹⁴ meters   The nucleus of a carbon atom

10 fermis

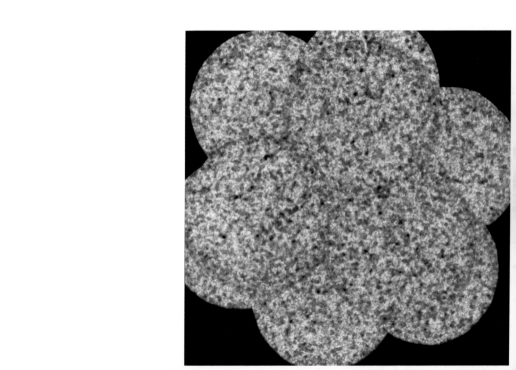

10^{-15} meters   A single proton fills the frame

1 fermi

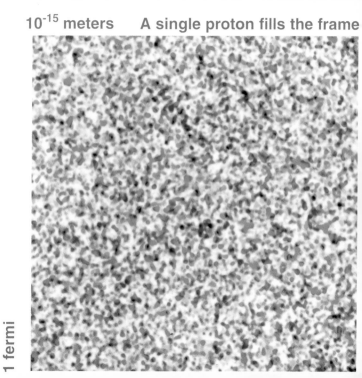

Printed in Hong Kong